To Megan
—G.M.

For Jimmy
—L.F.

Text copyright © 2002 by Grace Maccarone.
Illustrations copyright © 2002 by Laura Freeman.
All rights reserved. Published by Scholastic Inc.
Printed in the U.S.A.

ISBN 0-439-69318-7

SCHOLASTIC and associated logos and designs are trademarks and/or registered trademarks of Scholastic Inc.

6   7   8   9   10   23   12 11 10 09

The 100th Day

Story by Grace Maccarone
Illustrated by Laura Freeman

SCHOLASTIC INC.
New York Toronto London Auckland Sydney
Mexico City New Delhi Hong Kong Buenos Aires

Today is the 100th day of school
in Miss Hill's class.

Jill likes to make things.
She uses 100 beads
to make four necklaces.
Each necklace has 25 beads.

Jack does not want
to make necklaces.

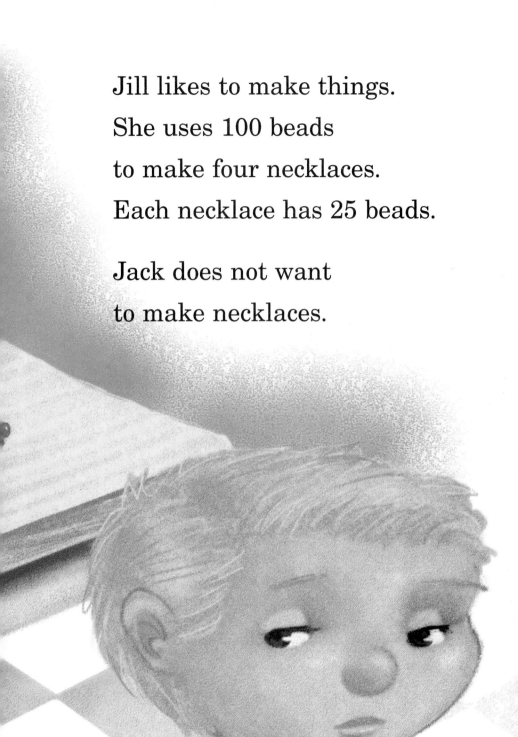

Ben likes to write stories.

He writes about 100 cats.

20 are black.

20 are orange.

20 are white.

20 are gray.

20 have stripes.

Jack does not want

to write a story.

Kate likes to draw.

She draws 100 stars.
50 are silver.
50 are gold.

Jack does not want
to draw.
What will Jack do?

Jack looks out the window.

He wants to run.

He wants to jump.

Jack has an idea.

He will jump to 100.

Can he do it?

Jill gets the rope.
She and Ben turn it.
Everyone counts together
as Jack jumps.

51 52 53 54 55 56
57 58 59 60 61 62
63 64 65 66 67
68 69 70 71 72
73 74 75 76 77 78
79 80 81 82 83
84 85 86 87 88
89 90 91 92
93 94
95 96 97 98 99

100!
Hooray for Jack!